The Official Study Guide for

WEEDING OUT THE
MYTHS
ABOUT
MARIJUANA

Expanded Edition:
A Medical and Biblical Perspective

The Official Study Guide for

WEEDING OUT THE
MYTHS
ABOUT
MARIJUANA

Expanded Edition:
A Medical and Biblical Perspective

RAYMOND WIGGINS, MD, MDiv

Torn Veil Publishing (TVP)
The Official Study Guide for Weeding Out the Myths About Marijuana, Expanded Edition: A Medical and Biblical Perspective

Published by Torn Veil Publishing in the United States of America.
tornveilpublishing.com

Details of stories in this book have been changed to protect the identities of those involved. All internet addresses and other references in this book are offered as resources. Inclusion of any resource does not imply endorsement by TVP, Dr. Wiggins, or anyone associated with them. Dr. Wiggins, TVP, nor anyone associated with them can be held responsible for the content of or warrant the accuracy of any resource.

The information contained in this book is for informational purposes only. No material in this book is intended to substitute for professional medical advice and should not be used to diagnose, treat, prevent, or cure any disease. Always seek the advice of your physician or other qualified healthcare providers with any questions you have regarding a medical condition or treatment before undertaking a new healthcare regimen. Never disregard professional medical advice or delay seeking it because of something you read in this book.

Cover design and interior design: Christy Day

ISBN: 978-1-7325816-6-1 (paperback)
ISBN: 978-1-7325816-8-5 (ebook)

Library of Congress Control Number: 2023942486

First printing 2024

Please visit drwiggins.com

Requests for information should be addressed to: info@tornveilpublishing.com

To my father and mother,
who gave me a love for learning
and set me on the firm foundation of God.

Contents

Study Guide Introduction

I developed this study guide, *The Official Study Guide for Weeding Out the Myths About Marijuana, Expanded Edition: A Medical and Biblical Perspective,* to give the reader of the book a chance to go deeper into the weeds regarding marijuana. I believe those who want to learn more and dig deeper into this subject, individually or in a group setting, will find this study guide informative and thought-provoking.

This study guide is an essential resource for small or large-group studies. Churches, schools, colleges and universities, addiction treatment and recovery programs, youth programs, and more can use it. Unfortunately, the Christian perspective presented in this study and book will likely keep this material from public schools and other public institutions. This study guide is useful for teens and young adults wanting to learn the truth about marijuana, parents and grandparents wanting to learn the truth about the devastating effects on their children and grandchildren, and anyone wanting to learn the truth about marijuana for their benefit and the benefit of those around them.

This study guide should only be used with the book *Weeding Out the Myths About Marijuana, Expanded Edition: A Medical and Biblical Perspective.* The exercises and questions will benefit little without the corresponding book.

Each chapter of this study guide correlates with a chapter of the book. Each chapter includes selected scripture, application, the main idea of the chapter, a chapter summary, chapter terms, questions, group discussion starters, and reflection. Space is provided to record answers to the questions and reflection about chapters.

While *Weeding Out the Myths About Marijuana* and this official study guide contain useful information about marijuana for all audiences, the book and this study guide are geared toward Christian audiences who esteem the Bible as God's Word. This series has other resources geared toward public schools and public institutions. See DrWiggins.com/books for all available options in this series.

I urge you to pray before reading each chapter of the book and ask God to guide you in understanding and interpreting the information and answering the questions in this study guide. If you are using this guide as a small or large group resource, be prepared for each meeting. Read the chapter and answer the corresponding questions, including the group discussion questions, before the meeting. Many people will not have time to answer every question. However, you will only get out of these resources and meetings what you put into them. Make an effort to reflect on and answer the questions. You will not regret learning as much as possible about this important subject.

The subject of marijuana can be a contentious one. If you are part of a group using the book *Weeding Out the Myths About Marijuana* and this study guide, you agree to the following group guidelines:

- Every member of the group listens with respect. It is acceptable to disagree, but personal attacks are never appropriate. Respectful debate may be appropriate as deemed proper by group leaders. Heated or disrespectful arguments and discourteous, non-Christian behavior of any type are never appropriate.

- Do not interrupt anyone who is talking. Only one person at a time may speak. Group leaders may interrupt as necessary for reasons such as time, respect, etc.

- Stay on the subject. Try to help your leader keep the conversation on the subject being discussed. No one person should dominate the conversation. Answers to questions should generally be no longer than sixty to ninety seconds, and stories should be shortened to include only relevant material.

o What is said in the meeting stays in the meeting. Personal information and stories are strictly confidential and may only be divulged as required by law or as deemed appropriate by all in the group.

o Group leaders have the final say. They may add to this list as necessary for their specific community needs. Always respect the decisions of group leaders. Their job is sometimes difficult, and they are human. Love and respect them. If you have a serious disagreement with them, respectfully discuss it with them outside of meeting time in a spirit of love and kindness.

Number of Sessions?

This guide has eleven chapters devoted to the book, with a study guide chapter devoted to the book's Introduction and each of the book's ten chapters.

Group leaders can easily tailor this guide to use with four to eleven sessions. Most groups will want to devote six to eleven sessions to this study and book. Breaking this study into eleven sessions allows for a very in-depth study. Cutting this study down to four sessions loses some depth but may be appropriate for some groups.

The following table will help leaders merge the appropriate chapters and tell which chapter or chapters should be covered in each session.

How to Combine Chapters to Have the Desired Number of Sessions

Number of Sessions Planned Book Chapter	4	6	8	11
Introduction	Session 1	Session 1	Session 1	Session 1
Chapter 1	Session 1	Session 1	Session 2	Session 2
Chapter 2	Session 1 or skip	Session 2 or skip	Session 2 or skip	Session 3
Chapter 3	Session 2	Session 2	Session 3	Session 4
Chapter 4	Session 2	Session 3	Session 4	Session 5
Chapter 5	Session 2	Session 3	Session 5	Session 6
Chapter 6	Session 2 or 3	Session 3 or 4	Session 5 or 6	Session 7
Chapter 7	Session 3	Session 4	Session 6	Session 8
Chapter 8	Session 3	Session 4	Session 6	Session 9
Chapter 9	Session 4	Session 5	Session 7	Session 10
Chapter 10	Session 4	Session 6	Session 8	Session 11

Study Plan

Book Introduction

For this session, please read the Prologue and Introduction in *Weeding Out the Myths About Marijuana, Expanded Edition: A Medical and Biblical Perspective*. Read the information in this study guide chapter and answer the corresponding questions.

As you read, ask God to open the eyes of your heart to the truths found in these resources. Reflect on what God shows you and write down those thoughts in the "Reflection" section.

Selected Scripture

"The first one to plead his cause seems right, until his neighbor comes and examines him." Proverbs 18:17

Application

In the battle for the mind, evidence is crucial. As a jury sits in a civil court of law, the plaintiff's attorneys present their case first. After hearing the evidence presented by the plaintiff's attorneys, jurors often believe the plaintiff should prevail. It is natural that after only hearing one side of an argument, the jurors' opinion is swayed to the plaintiff's side. Then, the defense attorneys argue for their client. The defense attorneys' goal is to convince jurors that the plaintiff's arguments are not valid, even absurd. The defense attorneys will systematically and methodically tear down each argument of the plaintiff. Once the defense has rested its case, the jury is often swayed to believe the defense should prevail.

In the court of public opinion regarding marijuana, only one side has had the vast majority of coverage. One side has been much more vocal. One side has been given a voice, and the other has been suppressed. Many advocates of marijuana have significant financial and political interests. With the help of many in the media and celebrities, they have done a much better job of presenting their case. They downplay the adverse effects of marijuana. They use the "It's my body. It's my life" argument to silence the voices of the opposition. This book and study will boldly go where no book or study has gone. They will look to science and the Bible to see if there is another side to this story.

I believe you will enjoy this book and companion study guide as much as I have enjoyed writing them. I pray the eyes of your heart are opened by the evidence contained in them.

Main Idea of Introduction

The Introduction to *Weeding Out the Myths About Marijuana, Expanded Edition: A Medical and Biblical Perspective* offers background information regarding marijuana, including defining terms and statistical evidence regarding the use and economics of marijuana.

Introduction Summary

The Introduction to *Weeding Out the Myths About Marijuana* discusses background information regarding the use of marijuana, a mind-altering drug derived from the Cannabis sativa plant. The Introduction offers many statistics regarding users and the economics (macroeconomics) of marijuana. Marijuana use is increasing rapidly. Eighteen percent of Americans have used marijuana in the past year as of 2020. Furthermore, the illegal sales of marijuana were estimated to be $60 billion in the U.S. in 2020, and legal sales of marijuana likely surpassed $33 billion by the end of 2022.

The marijuana plant contains about 540 chemical substances, of which approximately 120 are active substances—cannabinoids, including the active substances THC (tetrahydrocannabinol) and CBD (cannabidiol). THC is responsible for the mind-altering effects of marijuana, commonly referred to as the "marijuana high."

Marijuana has been used for at least 2,500 years, with evidence of its use in ancient rituals. Today, marijuana is primarily used for recreational purposes. The use of marijuana is still illegal under federal law in the United States, with marijuana being classified as a Schedule I drug, meaning it has no recognized medical use and a high potential for abuse.

Terms

Cannabinoids: The active substances in the cannabis plant. There are more than 120 known at this time. They include CBD and THC. The full effects on the body are not known.

Cannabis: Refers to any product that comes from the Cannabis sativa plant. Cannabis also refers to the Genus of the Cannabis sativa plant. The terms *marijuana* and *cannabis* are often used interchangeably.

Cannabis sativa Plant: also known as the "marijuana plant." It is the plant most often grown to produce marijuana.

CBD (cannabidiol): Considered to be non-psychoactive (non-mind-altering) cannabinoids (active substances in the cannabis plant), but the full effects are not known.

Marijuana: The parts of or the products from the Cannabis sativa plant with a higher THC (>0.3%) than hemp.

THC (tetrahydrocannabinol): The compound responsible for the mind-altering (psychoactive) effects of marijuana, otherwise known as the "marijuana high."

Questions

1. What are THC and CBD?

_____

_____

_____

_____

_____

2. What is the difference between cannabis and marijuana?

_____

_____

_____

_____

_____

3. What is the psychoactive (mind-altering) compound in marijuana?

_____

_____

_____

_____

_____

4.   How long has marijuana been used?

_____

_____

_____

_____

_____

5.   What is the meaning of a Schedule I drug classification?

_____

_____

_____

_____

_____

6.   What is the trend in marijuana use in the United States?

_____

_____

_____

_____

_____

7.   What percentage of Americans have used marijuana in the past year?

_____

_____

_____

_____

_____

8. What percentage of twelfth graders have used marijuana in the past year?

_____

_____

_____

_____

_____

Group Discussion

1. What is the difference between cannabis, cannabidiol (CBD), and cannabinoids?

_____

_____

_____

_____

_____

2. Why is it important that marijuana is a Schedule I drug?

_____

_____

_____

_____

_____

3. Is there a financial incentive for marijuana to be legalized, and who would benefit financially?

_____

_____

_____

_____

_____

4. Why are so many politicians behind the effort to legalize marijuana?

_____

_____

_____

_____

_____

5. Are you surprised by the statistics in this Introduction? If so, which statistic or statistics surprised you the most?

_____

_____

_____

_____

_____

6. Has marijuana negatively impacted your life or the life of anyone
    you know?

_____

_____

_____

_____

_____

Reflection

_____

_____

_____

_____

_____

_____

_____

_____

CHAPTER 1

Hidden Costs

Selected Scripture

"A prudent man foresees evil and hides himself, but the simple pass on and are punished. By humility and the fear of the Lord are riches and honor and life. Thorns and snares are in the way of the perverse; He who guards his soul will be far from them." Proverbs 22:3-5

Application

Prudent people see danger and avoid it. Foolish people see the danger and continue as if nothing is wrong. Perhaps they do not realize or perceive the true danger. They may know the dangers yet believe the benefits outweigh the risks.

As we will learn throughout this study guide and book, there are many pitfalls and dangers associated with marijuana. Those dangers far outweigh any perceived benefit. You may not be convinced at this point, but the evidence contained in this book is overwhelming.

Main Idea of Chapter

Marijuana leads to many hidden societal and economic costs. The societal and economic costs outweigh the benefits.

Chapter Summary

This chapter discusses the hidden costs of marijuana, which are often overlooked by proponents of legalization, who often focus on the perceived safety and neglect to see the negative consequences. The illegal and "legal" marijuana industries are associated with organized crime, which often operates with impunity and uses human trafficking victims to cultivate marijuana. Violence and crime increase with marijuana use, and it is a significant risk factor for domestic violence and too often leads to driving under the influence of marijuana. The legalization and decriminalization of marijuana have led to an increase in accidents and fatalities caused by impaired driving. Adolescent and young adult use of marijuana has increased in states where it has been legalized. Marijuana use has been linked to lower life satisfaction, poorer mental and physical health, relationship problems, academic and career difficulties, and job loss.

The economic costs of legalization are significant, and for every dollar gained in tax revenue, there is a cost of $4.50 to mitigate the effects of legalization. The chapter concludes that marijuana has negative consequences not only for users but also for their families, friends, and society as a whole.

Terms

DUI: "Driving under the influence" of a mind-altering substance.

Psychosis: A severe mental disorder in which a person loses the ability to recognize reality or relate to others. A common term used for psychosis is "crazy," although the word "crazy" has no official use in psychiatry.

Questions

1. What are examples of legal marijuana operations being controlled by politically connected players?

_____

_____

_____

_____

_____

2. Is marijuana use a significant risk factor for domestic violence and driving under the influence? Explain your answer.

_____

_____

_____

_____

_____

3. Do law enforcement officers generally agree that the legalization of marijuana and its use increase crime?

_____

_____

_____

_____

_____

4. Is cannabis often cultivated by human trafficking victims? Explain how modern-day slavery is pervasive in the marijuana industry.

_____

_____

_____

_____

_____

5. Has there been an increase in automobile accidents caused by those under the influence of marijuana in recent years? How has this significantly impacted states where marijuana has been legalized?

_____

_____

_____

_____

_____

6. Has marijuana legalization led to increased adolescent and young adult use? Why?

_____

_____

_____

_____

_____

7. According to the Centennial Institute study, for every dollar gained in tax revenue, Coloradans spent approximately how much to mitigate the effects of legalization?

_____

_____

_____

_____

_____

Group Discussion

1. Describe the association between organized crime and the illegal and legal marijuana industries.

_____

_____

_____

_____

_____

2. Proponents of marijuana legalization argue that tax revenue from legalized marijuana is a reason to legalize marijuana. How do social and economic costs overshadow these benefits? ($4.50 cost for every dollar of tax revenue)

_____

_____

_____

_____

_____

3. Does marijuana lead to a better life? If you answer yes, why do studies show marijuana is associated with problems such as lower life satisfaction, poorer mental and physical health, relationship problems, academic and career difficulties, and job loss?

_____

_____

_____

_____

_____

4. Is driving under the influence of marijuana dangerous? How does it affect areas of the brain that control skills required for safe driving?

_____

_____

_____

_____

_____

5. Were you surprised by the violence associated with marijuana? Why or why not?

_____

_____

_____

_____

_____

6. Knowing the statistics already noted in the book regarding marijuana's effects on others, is the "It is my body; it is my life" argument appropriate regarding marijuana? Why or why not?

_____

_____

_____

_____

_____

7. Is marijuana use linked to a higher likelihood of dropping out of school and more job absences, accidents, and injuries? If so, why do you believe this is true?

_____

_____

_____

_____

_____

Reflection

_____

_____

_____

_____

_____

_____

_____

_____

_____

_____

_____

_____

_____

_____

_____

_____

_____

_____

CHAPTER 2

How Weed Works

Selected Scripture

" . . . always be ready to give a defense to everyone who asks you a reason for the hope that is in you . . . ." 1 Peter 3:15

Application

The Bible is full of scriptures that tell us to be prepared for various tasks. The above scripture, 1 Peter 3:15, refers to being prepared to share the Gospel of Jesus Christ at all times. Second Timothy 4:2 says to be prepared to preach the Word at all times and in all circumstances. Matthew 24:44 says to be prepared for the return of the Son of Man, Jesus Christ. 1 Peter 1:13 says to prepare our minds for action and be sober. The Bible is clear. We must be prepared. Conversations about marijuana can sometimes turn to the spiritual aspects. This book and study help us navigate those conversations. We should be prepared to answer questions about marijuana and its dangers and present the Gospel when the door is opened.

Main Idea of Chapter

There are many effects of marijuana on the body, particularly the brain. This chapter explains how marijuana exerts its effects.

Chapter Summary

This chapter contains information needed to prepare you for the rest of the book and for discussions you may have with those knowledgeable about marijuana. Do not get lost in the details—the weeds. Just know that any knowledge you gain here will benefit you later.

This chapter explores how marijuana works in the body. Cannabinoids, including THC, interact with cannabinoid receptors (CB) in the central nervous system. CB1 receptors are primarily found in the brain, while CB2 receptors mainly reside in the immune system. THC, the main psychoactive component in marijuana, mimics an endogenous (made in the body) cannabinoid called anandamide, which unlocks CB receptors in the brain and affects various brain functions, such as memory, attention, movement, and coordination. THC also causes dopamine release, leading to pleasure and teaching the brain to repeat the rewarding behavior, ultimately resulting in decreased production of and sensitivity to dopamine and marijuana's addictive properties.

When smoked, THC reaches the brain within thirty seconds of inhalation, and brain concentration peaks between thirty to sixty minutes, with effects lasting three to four hours. Edibles have a much slower onset, leading to highly variable and potentially dangerous effects. Unlike alcohol, marijuana has an extremely variable effect from person to person, making it challenging to determine sobriety or intoxication levels.

Understanding how marijuana exerts its effects is essential to understanding how it affects the body and the mind and is crucial when discussing the subject of marijuana with individuals knowledgeable about it.

Terms

Anandamide: An endogenous (made in the body) cannabinoid. THC is similar to this molecule.

Dopamine: Also known as "the pleasure chemical." A hormone and neurotransmitter that plays many functions in the body. Marijuana leads to increased dopamine, but the body quickly sees it has too much. So, it produces less and becomes less sensitive to dopamine. This can lead to many negative effects, including mental health issues and addiction. (Cleveland Clinic Health Library Articles: Dopamine, https://my.clevelandclinic.org/health/articles/22581-dopamine).

Endogenous: A substance made within the body.

Hormones: Chemicals that affect distant cells, usually traveling through the bloodstream.

Marijuana Edibles: Marijuana-infused substances meant to be ingested, such as brownies and gummies.

Neurons: Nerve cells.

Neurotransmitters: Chemical messengers that allow nerves to communicate with each other and other target cells.

Synapses: Gaps between neurons where neurotransmitters communicate.

Receptors: Molecules on cells that act as a lock on which neurotransmitters and hormones act as a key to unlock.

Questions

These questions may be too in-depth for some groups. Choose those questions related to your level of understanding. If you are part of a group, you may want to ask your group leader which questions to answer. Again, do not get bogged down in this chapter.

1. What are hormones, and how do they affect distant cells?

_____

_____

_____

_____

_____

2. What are neurotransmitters, and how do they communicate between neurons?

_____

_____

_____

_____

_____

3. How do drugs interact with receptors on the surface of cells, and what effects can they have on the activity of the cell?

_____

_____

_____

_____

_____

4. What are cannabinoids, and how do they affect the central nervous system?

_____

_____

_____

_____

_____

5. Where are cannabinoid receptors found in the brain, and what functions do they affect?

_____

_____

_____

_____

_____

6. What is anandamide, and how is it related to THC?

_____

_____

_____

_____

_____

7. What are the differences in the onset and duration of effect of marijuana when smoked versus ingested in edibles?

_____

_____

_____

_____

_____

8. How do drugs typically exert their effects on the body?

_____

_____

_____

_____

_____

9. How does THC affect memory, focus, coordination, attention, and anxiety?

_____

_____

_____

_____

_____

10. What are the implications of the increased dopamine release seen with marijuana use?

_____

_____

_____

_____

_____

11. How might the information in this chapter help you later?

_____

_____

_____

_____

_____

12. What were the implications of finding anandamide?

_____

_____

_____

_____

_____

13. How do the effects of marijuana vary from person to person, and why is it difficult to predict the level of intoxication?

_____

_____

_____

_____

_____

14. What are the implications of person-to-person variability for impairment and safety?

_____

_____

_____

_____

15. With the understanding of how marijuana works in the body, how does this knowledge help inform discussions around its clinical effects on the mind and body?

_____

_____

_____

_____

Group Discussion

1. How does THC affect dopamine release in the brain, and what are the consequences of repeated stimulation of the reward system?

_____

_____

_____

_____

_____

2. How does the variability of the effects of marijuana from person to person differ from that of alcohol, and what are the implications of this difference?

_____

_____

_____

_____

_____

3. When smoking marijuana, how long does it typically take to feel the effects?

_____

_____

_____

_____

_____

4. What are some differences between ingesting marijuana through edibles versus smoking it in terms of onset and duration of effect?

_____

_____

_____

_____

_____

5. Why might ingesting marijuana through edibles lead to an increased risk of overdose?

_____

_____

_____

_____

_____

6. THC affects many bodily functions. How many can you list?

_____

_____

_____

_____

7. What are some of the implications of THC impairment?

_____

_____

_____

_____

_____

Reflection

_____

_____

_____

_____

_____

_____

_____

_____

_____

_____

_____

CHAPTER 3

Medical Perspective

Selected Scripture

"Or do you not know that your body is the temple of the Holy Spirit who is in you, whom you have from God, and you are not your own? For you were bought at a price; therefore glorify God in your body and in your spirit, which are God's." 1 Corinthians 6:19-20.

Application

Many Old Testament laws were, at least in part, regarding health: taking a sabbath rest, quarantining the sick, washing one's hands before eating, etc. While many of these laws had spiritual meanings, they also served to keep those who kept them physically healthy. God wanted His people to be healthy.

While the above scripture, 1 Corinthians 6:19-20, directly addresses sexual immorality, this scripture can be rightly applied to physical well-being in general. Just as God calls us to live lives of sexual purity to avoid destroying our bodily temples, we should not destroy those temples through drugs, alcohol, overeating, or any other means. We should not worship our bodies but take care of them. As we will soon see, we dishonor our bodies and God when we put marijuana in our bodies.

Main Idea of Chapter

This chapter evaluates marijuana's effects on the body. Although many people see marijuana as benign, marijuana significantly negatively affects many bodily systems and processes.

Chapter Summary

This chapter discusses the medical aspects of marijuana, including its effects on the lungs, heart, immune system, and brain. Marijuana potency has increased significantly over the years, leading to a higher risk of dependency and adverse effects. Smoking marijuana damages the lungs and increases the risk of lung cancer. It also has devastating effects on the heart, with recent studies showing increased risks of heart attacks and other cardiac issues.

Marijuana also weakens the immune system and negatively impacts brain function, particularly in areas responsible for memory, attention, learning, and decision-making. The effects are more significant in young users whose brains are still developing.

From a medical standpoint, there are many problems and risks associated with marijuana and no real benefits. Here is a summary of some of the medical issues that marijuana causes. Marijuana leads to early heart attacks, second heart attacks, heart failure, arrhythmias (often dangerous irregular heart rhythms), sudden cardiac death, lung cancer, asthma, bronchitis, immune system problems, decreased fertility, genomic and epigenomic damage, poor oral health, strokes, lower IQ, problems with thinking, memory, learning, attention, decision-making, coordination, emotions, reaction time, confusion, and sleep disturbances. Marijuana is not something you should want in your body.

Terms

Joint: A rolled marijuana cigarette.

Potency: Related to the percent THC. The higher the percent THC, the greater the effects and side effects. It was 1% to 3% in most joints at Woodstock (1969). Now, it averages 22%.

Questions

1. Discuss the relationship between marijuana use and the immune system. How does marijuana impact the body's ability to fight off disease and infection?

   _____

   _____

   _____

   _____

   _____

2. What are the effects of marijuana on brain function, particularly in young people and developing brains?

   _____

   _____

   _____

   _____

   _____

3. How does marijuana use impact academic performance and cognitive abilities, such as creativity and intelligence?

_____

_____

_____

_____

_____

4. How does marijuana use before and during pregnancy affect the development of the baby's brain and the child's future cognitive abilities and behavior?

_____

_____

_____

_____

_____

5. How does marijuana-induced psychosis manifest in terms of emotional, cognitive (thinking, knowing, and perceiving), and behavioral symptoms?

_____

_____

_____

_____

_____

6. Can you explain the role of dopamine in marijuana's impact on the brain's reward system and its potential long-term effects?

_____

_____

_____

_____

_____

7. What is the "vicious cycle" described in the scenario involving marijuana use to reduce anxiety, and how does this contribute to increased dependency on the drug?

_____

_____

_____

_____

_____

Group Discussion

1. Considering the potential risks and consequences of marijuana use, how can public awareness and education be improved to prevent or minimize these negative outcomes?

_____

_____

_____

_____

_____

2. How has the potency of marijuana changed since 1969, and why
   is this significant for users' health?

_____

_____

_____

_____

_____

3. What are the known lung effects of smoking marijuana, and how
   do they compare to smoking cigarettes?

_____

_____

_____

_____

_____

4. How does marijuana affect the heart, and what are the potential
   risks of marijuana use on cardiovascular health?

_____

_____

_____

_____

_____

5. Name as many of the medical problems and risks listed in the
    book as you can. How many can you list? (You may make this
    a contest, with each person or group writing the list on paper.
    The person or group who writes the largest number of problems
    or risks wins.)

_____

_____

_____

_____

_____

Reflection

_____

_____

_____

_____

_____

_____

_____

_____

_____

_____

_____

_____

_____

_____

_____

_____

_____

_____

_____

_____

_____

_____

_____

_____

_____

_____

_____

_____

CHAPTER 4

Mental Health

Selected Scripture

"Be anxious for nothing, but in everything by prayer and supplication, with thanksgiving, let your requests be made known to God; and the peace of God, which surpasses all understanding, will guard your hearts and minds through Christ Jesus." Philippians 4:6-7

Application

At least a component of mental health is spiritual, just as every aspect of life has a spiritual component. When you have anxiety, depression, or suicidal thoughts, pray and earnestly ask God for His help and healing. Thank Him for what He has done and will do in your life. He promises that His peace will guard your heart and mind. Scripture is confirmed by science. A 2021 meta-analysis of sixty-two studies showed a tremendous decrease in depression in those who have gratitude. Several studies have shown a link between gratitude and decreased anxiety, as well as a better overall outlook on life. Practice gratitude. According to the Bible and science, it can improve your mental health. (JA Iodice et al., "The Association between Gratitude and Depression: A Meta-Analysis" (2021) International Journal of Depression and Anxiety 4:024, The Association between Gratitude and Depression: A Meta-Analysis (clinmedjournals.org). N Khorrami, "Gratitude Helps Curb Anxiety," Psychology Today (July 20, 2020), https://www.psychologytoday.com/us/blog/comfort-gratitude/202007/gratitude-helps-curb-anxiety. "Giving Thanks Can Make You Happier," Harvard Health, (August 14, 2021), https://www.health.harvard.edu/healthbeat/giving-thanks-can-make-you-happier.)

Main Idea of Chapter

This chapter evaluates marijuana's effects on mental health. Although many people see marijuana as benign, marijuana significantly negatively affects mental health.

Chapter Summary

This chapter discusses the mental health effects of marijuana. Keep in mind that marijuana potency has increased significantly over the years, leading to a higher risk of dependency and adverse mental health effects. Marijuana has been linked to various mental health issues, such as depression, anxiety, panic attacks, paranoia, suicidal thoughts, and psychosis.

Marijuana-induced psychosis can cause various adverse effects, such as loss of control, anxiety, paranoia, hallucinations, and sleep disturbances (difficulty falling asleep and staying asleep). It is associated with a higher risk of schizophrenia. Marijuana affects the brain's reward system through dopamine release, leading to addiction and reduced pleasure. Users often get caught in a cycle of using marijuana to reduce anxiety but end up feeling more anxious and dependent on the drug.

Marijuana is also linked to Amotivational Syndrome, which results in a lack of motivation, social withdrawal, and impaired memory. Contrary to popular belief, marijuana is addictive, both psychologically and physically. Cannabis Withdrawal Syndrome (CWS) includes symptoms like irritability, insomnia (difficulty falling asleep and staying asleep), and severe cravings. Approximately 30% of users suffer from addiction, known as Cannabis Use Disorder (CUD) or Marijuana Use Disorder (MUD), which can negatively impact daily functioning and responsibilities.

From a mental health standpoint, there are many problems and risks associated with marijuana and no real benefits. Here is a summary of some of the adverse mental health effects of marijuana. Marijuana leads to social withdrawal, depression, anxiety, fear, panic attacks, social anxiety, paranoia, hallucinations, schizophrenia, and suicide. Marijuana is not something you should want in your body.

Terms

Cannabis Use Disorder: Also known as Marijuana Use Disorder, CUD, or MUD. It is the medical term for addiction to marijuana.

Schizophrenia: A severe form of psychosis involving hallucinations, delusions, and disorganized thinking that lasts at least six months. Patients are unable to determine what is real versus what is not. It may include negative symptoms such as lack of interest, social withdrawal, inability to feel pleasure, and lack of motivation.

Schizophreniform Disorder: A form of psychosis that is similar to schizophrenia but has a shorter duration.

Questions

1. What are the various mental health effects of marijuana use, and how does the risk of these effects change with the frequency of use?

_____

_____

_____

_____

2. How does Amotivational Syndrome relate to marijuana use, and what are the common symptoms of this syndrome?

_____

_____

_____

_____

_____

3. Discuss the differences between physical and psychological addiction to marijuana. Would you want either one?

_____

_____

_____

_____

_____

4. What is Cannabis Withdrawal Syndrome (CWS), and how do its symptoms and severity vary based on factors such as frequency of use, potency, and length of use?

_____

_____

_____

_____

_____

5. How is Cannabis Use Disorder (CUD) or Marijuana Use Disorder (MUD) defined, and what are the common symptoms of this addiction?

_____

_____

_____

_____

_____

6. In what ways can marijuana addiction affect a person's personal and professional life?

_____

_____

_____

_____

_____

7. Discuss the causal relationship between marijuana use and psychosis. Can marijuana-induced psychosis have long-lasting or permanent effects?

_____

_____

_____

_____

_____

Group Discussion

1. Were you inspired by Victoria's Story? What inspired you, and what did you learn?

_____

_____

_____

_____

_____

2. What is the connection between marijuana use and the risk of developing schizophrenia, and how does the risk vary depending on the age of first use and frequency of use?

_____

_____

_____

_____

_____

3. Name as many of the mental health problems and risks listed in the book as you can. How many can you list? (You may make this a contest, with each person or group writing the list on paper. The person or group who writes the largest number of problems or risks wins.)

_____

_____

_____

_____

_____

Reflection

_____

_____

_____

_____

_____

_____

_____

_____

_____

_____

_____

_____

_____

_____

_____

CHAPTER 5

Medical Miscellaneous

Selected Scripture

"Stand fast therefore in the liberty by which Christ has made us free, and do not be entangled again with a yoke of bondage." Galatians 5:1

Application

Approximately 30% of those who smoke marijuana are addicted and cannot stop. This addiction is called Cannabis Use Disorder. It has several other names, such as CUD, Marijuana Use Disorder, and MUD. The symptoms can include a sense of craving the drug, problems with day-to-day functioning and responsibilities, giving up activities that were once enjoyed, and physical tolerance to the drug, which means users need to consume more and more to achieve the same high.

When people play around with marijuana, they never know if they will be a part of that 30%. Why take the chance? God does not want anyone to be a slave to sin. He wants everyone to be free in Him. Paul warns in Galatians 5:1 not to be entangled again by the yoke of bondage. Addiction is bondage.

Main Idea of Chapter

This chapter examines miscellaneous marijuana topics from a medical and scientific perspective. It covers hot topics such as edibles, vaping, synthetic marijuana, medical marijuana, CBD, and delta-8 and determines that marijuana is a gateway drug.

Chapter Summary

This chapter investigates various marijuana-related subjects from medical and scientific viewpoints, such as edibles, vaping, synthetic marijuana, medical marijuana, CBD, and delta-8.

Edibles, such as gummies, candies, brownies, and beverages called "liquid edibles" or "drinkables," contain varying amounts of THC or CBD infused into the food. The unpredictability of edibles' potency can lead to dangerous consequences, including overdoses and fatalities.

Vaping marijuana has grown in popularity, but it carries numerous risks, including e-cigarette or vaping use-associated lung injury (EVALI) and exposure to toxic compounds. Vaping can also lead to psychosis, paranoia, and cannabis hyperemesis syndrome (uncontrolled vomiting) due to high THC concentrations.

Synthetic marijuana, also known as synthetic cannabis, spice, or K2, is a manufactured substance mimicking THC's effects. However, it is more potent and has more severe and unpredictable consequences, including anxiety, paranoia, hallucinations, heart attacks, seizures, memory loss, and even death. Synthetic marijuana has been linked to persistent psychosis and structural brain abnormalities.

Medical marijuana is often prescribed for pain and nausea, but scientific evidence supporting its effectiveness is lacking. Smoking marijuana is not FDA-approved for any medical use, and its safety and efficacy have not been scientifically established. The FDA has not approved the cannabis plant for any medical use, but it has approved a few drugs, such as Epidiolex, Marinol, Syndros, and

Cesamet, for specific conditions. None of these drugs contain a natural form of THC.

CBD, the non-THC active portion of marijuana, is legal in most places. However, research on its safety and effectiveness is limited, and it can cause various side effects and interact with other medications, potentially leading to deadly effects. CBD products' purity and dosage are often unreliable, and some may contain THC.

Marijuana is a dangerous drug in and of itself, and studies indicate it serves as a gateway to other illicit drugs. Those who use marijuana are more likely to use and become addicted to opioids and other substances. Despite misconceptions, marijuana is not an innocent drug and carries potentially permanent and deadly effects.

Terms

Gateway Drug: Any drug that leads to the use of other drugs.

Medical Marijuana: Marijuana used for medical purposes. Contrary to popular belief, the FDA has not approved the cannabis plant for any medical use.

Synthetic Marijuana: Known by many other names, including synthetic cannabis, SC, spice, and K2. It is a manufactured substance similar to THC, the compound in marijuana that causes the high. These drugs are not marijuana, but they are more powerful and have even more unpredictable and severe effects.

Questions

1. What are the main differences between consuming marijuana through edibles and smoking it in terms of onset and duration? Why is this important?

_____

_____

_____

2. How does the varying potency of edibles contribute to the risk of overdose?

_____

_____

_____

_____

_____

3. Can you discuss the dangers associated with vaping marijuana and the potential long-term health risks?

_____

_____

_____

_____

_____

4. Is vaping THC safer than smoking marijuana? How is this misconception harmful?

_____

_____

_____

_____

_____

5. Can you explain the dangers associated with synthetic marijuana, including the potential for acute and persistent psychosis?

_____

_____

_____

_____

_____

6. What are the risks associated with CBD's interaction with other medications, such as blood thinners?

_____

_____

_____

_____

_____

7. How do the purity and dosage reliability issues impact the safety and effectiveness of CBD and delta-8 products?

_____

_____

_____

_____

_____

8. Is there any evidence to support the claim that marijuana is a
    gateway drug?

_____

_____

_____

_____

_____

Group Discussion

1. How do the neurologic and psychiatric effects of synthetic can-
    nabis compare to those of natural marijuana?

_____

_____

_____

_____

_____

2. Is there any credible research supporting smoking marijuana for
    various medical conditions, such as cancer, epilepsy, or asthma?

_____

_____

_____

_____

_____

3. How effective is marijuana in treating pain, and are there better
   alternatives?

_____

_____

_____

_____

_____

4. How does marijuana use increase the likelihood of using other drugs,
   such as opioids, in the future? Does this make it a gateway drug?

_____

_____

_____

_____

_____

5. Is there other research supporting the idea that marijuana is a
   gateway drug?

_____

_____

_____

_____

_____

6. How does the promotion of marijuana as a safe drug contribute to the spread of misinformation about its risks and potential harms?

_____

_____

_____

_____

_____

7. Should the medical and scientific community work to dispel myths and educate the public about the dangers of marijuana use? Should the Christian community do the same?

_____

_____

_____

_____

_____

8. Considering the dangers and lack of proven benefits, what steps should be taken to prevent the widespread use of marijuana and its derivatives?

_____

_____

_____

_____

_____

9. Does the fact that marijuana is "natural" mean it is safe?

_____

_____

_____

_____

10. Is the comparison of medical marijuana, CBD, and delta-8 to miracle elixirs and snake oil appropriate? Why?

_____

_____

_____

_____

_____

Reflection

_____

_____

_____

_____

_____

_____

_____

_____

_____

_____

_____

_____

_____

_____

_____

_____

_____

_____

_____

CHAPTER 6

At What Cost?

Selected Scripture

"The Lord is near to those who have a broken heart and saves such as have a contrite spirit." Psalm 34:18

Application

Since the fall in the Garden of Eden, there has been heartache. God never promises us there will be no storms. He says in this world, we will have trouble (John 16:33), but He does promise peace in the midst of storms. The family members who told the stories in this chapter were devastated by the consequences brought about by marijuana use. Eventually, they found strength and peace in God. No matter how dark the night or how tragic the situation, God promises to be there with us (Cf. Hebrews 13:5). When our hearts are broken, He is our source of peace. When there seems to be no hope, He is our hope. When we have lost all joy, He gives joy (Romans 15:13, John 14:27, Psalm 46:1). When we feel anxious or afraid, God wants us to call on Him. He promises to be there when we do and to give us His peace that passes understanding (Philippians 4:6-7, Mark 4:37-41).

Main Idea of Chapter

The chapter examines the cost of a lost or devastated life and determines that no dollar amount can be placed on it. The cost is immeasurable.

Chapter Summary

No amount of money can replace a life. The cost of a lost or devastated life is immeasurable. In this chapter, we hear the stories of marijuana's devastating effects on users and their families.

In the first story, a mother tells the tragic story of a fourteen-year-old young man from a great family who started smoking marijuana recreationally. He obtained the marijuana as a teen at a party from someone who had a medical marijuana card. Then, he obtained his own card and began to sell marijuana. He began having increased anxiety and developed cannabis-induced psychosis. He lost his real friends and became reclusive. He took his life by jumping from a parking garage.

In the second story, a husband tells the story of his fifty-year-old wife with no history of psychosis. They had a blissful marriage. She began to smoke marijuana to reduce anxiety, but marijuana worsened her anxiety and eventually led to cannabis-induced psychosis. She exhibited bizarre and violent behavior. She threatened to kill and mutilate her husband, her adult children, and others and was physically violent toward her husband and others. She was involuntarily institutionalized eleven times. Each time she was off marijuana, she would return to normal. She never understood marijuana was the problem and not the solution to her mental health issues, so this led to a never-ending cycle of psychosis and sanity.

Terms

No new terms were introduced in this chapter.

Questions

1. Do these stories reinforce what you have learned in the book?

    _____

    _____

    _____

    _____

    _____

2. Do these stories impact your feelings about the legalization of marijuana?

    _____

    _____

    _____

    _____

    _____

3. Would you have had as much patience with your son as Laura Stack had with Johnny?

    _____

    _____

    _____

    _____

4. Would you have had as much patience with your spouse as the narrator of the second story?

_____

_____

_____

_____

_____

5. What did you learn from the first story?

_____

_____

_____

_____

_____

6. What did you learn from the second story?

_____

_____

_____

_____

7. How could Johnny and Lynn have avoided these tragic outcomes in their lives?

_____

_____

_____

_____

_____

8. Have you ever had a time in your life when everything seemed to go wrong, and hope seemed lost, but you still had peace? What was the source of that peace?

_____

_____

_____

_____

_____

Group Discussion

1. Which has impacted you more in the book, the statistics or the stories?

_____

_____

_____

_____

_____

2. Which story in this chapter impacted you more? Why?

_____

_____

_____

_____

_____

3. Discuss the strength of these narrators.

_____

_____

_____

_____

_____

4. If this was a story of your family member, would you be able to tell these stories to others?

_____

_____

_____

_____

_____

5. Can you apply anything from what you learned in the first story to your life?

_____

_____

_____

_____

_____

6. Is there anything you can apply to your life from what you learned in the second story?

_____

_____

_____

_____

_____

7. How could Johnny have avoided this tragic outcome? Lynn?

_____

_____

_____

_____

_____

8. Who or what is to blame for these disastrous outcomes?

_____

_____

_____

_____

_____

9.

10. Could education regarding the risks of marijuana have saved these users from these tragic outcomes?

_____

_____

_____

_____

_____

Reflection

_____

_____

_____

_____

_____

_____

_____

_____

_____

_____

_____

_____

_____

_____

_____

_____

_____

_____

_____

_____

_____

_____

_____

_____

_____

_____

CHAPTER 7

Does the Bible Address Marijuana?

Selected Scripture

"And that from childhood you have known the Holy Scriptures, which are able to make you wise for salvation through faith which is in Christ Jesus. All Scripture is given by inspiration of God, and is profitable for doctrine, for reproof, for correction, for instruction in righteousness, that the man of God may be complete, thoroughly equipped for every good work." 2 Timothy 3:15-17

Application

We find the sufficiency of Scripture in 2 Timothy 3:15-17. The doctrine of the sufficiency of Scripture says we can be thoroughly equipped for every good work and be complete simply through the Scripture. That means it is sufficient in itself to help us tackle any problem that comes our way. This passage also leads us to the inspiration, inerrancy, and infallibility of the Bible. Inerrancy means the Bible is without error. Infallibility means the Bible, properly interpreted, will not lead anyone astray. Because God is perfect and the Bible is God-breathed, it is without error and will not lead us astray. Because the Bible is God-breathed, it is the inspired Word of God. Cf. 2 Peter 1:20-21.

Main Idea of Chapter

The Bible addresses many aspects of marijuana without explicitly using the words "marijuana" or "cannabis." God's Word expressly addresses sobriety and other issues directly related to marijuana.

Chapter Summary

The Bible is a practical guidebook for life that concisely covers all areas of life. While the Bible may not specifically mention the words marijuana or cannabis, the Bible does tell us to be sober at all times, and we cannot use marijuana and stay sober. Being drunk and being high are both terms for not being sober. Lack of sobriety leads to many problems, and the Bible calls drunkenness a sin.

Some people argue that alcohol and marijuana are essentially the same, and since the Bible does not explicitly ban alcohol for all uses, the Bible does not ban marijuana. However, the Bible does call drunkenness a sin, and being high is not being sober.

The Bible does not prohibit all use of alcohol, but the Bible does contain strong warnings about the dangers of alcohol, which often destroys lives and causes untold pain. So, many Christians choose not to drink alcohol. The next chapter will give specific reasons why the Bible strongly warns against and forbids marijuana use.

Terms

Inerrancy of the Bible: It is without error.

Infallibility of the Bible: It will not lead us astray or cause us to fall.

Inspiration of the Bible: It is written by God. Literally God-breathed (2 Timothy 3:16).

Sufficiency of the Bible: It is sufficient to address every aspect of life and to equip the believer for every good work.

Questions

1. Does the Bible say anything about the subject of marijuana?

_____

_____

_____

_____

_____

2. How can we apply the biblical concept of sobriety to the use of marijuana?

_____

_____

_____

_____

_____

3. Why is it incorrect to substitute marijuana into biblical passages that speak of alcohol?

_____

_____

_____

_____

_____

4. Can a person use alcohol and not be drunk? Can a person smoke marijuana and not get high? With that in mind, how does the Bible's stance on alcohol differ from its stance on marijuana?

_____

_____

_____

_____

_____

5. How does the legality of alcohol and marijuana impact the biblical perspective on their use?

_____

_____

_____

_____

_____

6. In what ways does the Bible warn against the use of alcohol, even though it does not strictly prohibit its use?

_____

_____

_____

_____

_____

7. How can we apply biblical principles to contemporary issues not explicitly mentioned in the Bible?

_____

_____

_____

_____

8. How does the Bible's treatment of pornography relate to its treatment of marijuana?

_____

_____

_____

_____

9. In what ways can biblical teachings help us navigate the complex and ever-changing world of illicit drugs?

_____

_____

_____

_____

_____

10. How does the Bible's practical and concise manner help guide our understanding of every life topic?

_____

_____

_____

_____

_____

11. Has your life or the life of anyone you know been negatively affected by alcohol?

_____

_____

_____

_____

_____

12. Has your life or the life of anyone you know been negatively affected by marijuana?

_____

_____

_____

_____

_____

Group Discussion

1. How can the Bible be used as a guidebook for life when it does not directly address every subject known to humankind?

_____

_____

_____

_____

_____

2. Why does the Bible not directly cover, by name, every subject we will ever face?

_____

_____

_____

_____

_____

3. How large would the Bible need to be to cover every subject known to humanity, past, present, and future?

_____

_____

_____

_____

_____

4. Does the Bible use the words "marijuana" or "cannabis?"

_____

_____

_____

_____

_____

5. If not, how does the Bible address the subject of marijuana without explicitly using the words "marijuana" or "cannabis?"

_____

_____

_____

_____

_____

6. Should biblical teachings impact personal decisions, such as whether or not to drink alcohol or use marijuana? What or Who gives the Bible its authority?

_____

_____

_____

_____

_____

7. Has alcohol negatively impacted your life or the life of anyone you know?

_____

_____

_____

_____

_____

8. We asked the following question in week one. Has marijuana negatively impacted your life or the life of anyone you know? Would anyone else like to answer this question?

_____

_____

_____

_____

_____

Reflection

_____

_____

_____

_____

_____

_____

_____

_____

_____

_____

_____

_____

_____

_____

_____

_____

_____

_____

CHAPTER 8

Biblical Reasons to Say No

Selected Scripture

"The lazy man will not plow because of winter; He will beg during harvest and have nothing." Proverbs 20:4

Application

Amotivational syndrome, which marijuana causes, is a syndrome of laziness and doing less than one's best. God does not tolerate laziness. He wants His children to do everything with excellence. Colossians 3:23 says, "Whatever you do, work at it with all your heart, as working for the Lord."

The Bible has many warnings about the consequences of laziness. Laziness leads to poverty. Proverbs 14:23 says, "In all labor there is profit, but mere talk leads only to poverty." Laziness leads to hunger. Proverbs 20:4 says, "The lazy one does not plow after the autumn, so he begs during the harvest and has nothing." Laziness ends in slavery. Proverbs 12:24 says, "The hand of the diligent will rule, but the lazy man will be put to forced labor."

Main Idea of Chapter

There are many specific reasons the Bible gives to say no to marijuana. This chapter covers six.

Chapter Summary

The Bible, although not explicitly mentioning marijuana, gives guidance regarding the subject. There are several reasons from a Christian perspective not to use marijuana. First, our bodies are the temple of the Holy Spirit, and using marijuana dishonors our bodies due to its harmful effects. Second, marijuana leads to laziness, which the Bible condemns as it implores us to work with excellence and avoid laziness. Third, marijuana can lead to addiction, making a person a slave to sin, contrary to the freedom Christ offers. Fourth, Christians should rely on God for peace and joy instead of seeking them through mind-altering substances like marijuana. People using these substances are seeking solutions to problems only God can fix. Fifth, God calls Christians to obey the government. Marijuana is still illegal under federal law, and it is still illegal under state and local law in many places. Sixth, the Bible calls for Christians to be sober at all times.

Many passages emphasize sobriety; being high from marijuana is a lack of sobriety. Thus, the Bible's message is clear: be sober and avoid marijuana use.

Terms

Ordained: Ordered or decreed.

Schedule I Drug: A drug with no recognized medical use and high abuse potential. Illegal under federal law. Marijuana is a Schedule I drug.

Sober: Not drunk or high. Mind not altered by substances such as alcohol or drugs. Earnestly thoughtful character or demeanor. Marked by temperance, moderation, or seriousness.

Questions

1. How does the Bible provide guidance regarding marijuana use?

_____

_____

_____

_____

_____

2. How does marijuana use lead to laziness, and what does the Bible say about laziness?

_____

_____

_____

_____

_____

3. How do the teachings in Isaiah 9:6, John 14:27, Psalm 16:11, Philippians 4:6, and Galatians 5:22 demonstrate the importance of relying on God for peace and joy?

    _____

    _____

    _____

    _____

    _____

4. How do federal and state laws regarding marijuana impact a Christian's decision to use or avoid marijuana?

    _____

    _____

    _____

    _____

5. Why does the Bible call for Christians to be sober at all times, and how does this relate to marijuana use?

    _____

    _____

    _____

    _____

6. What Bible passages emphasize the importance of sobriety for Christians?

_____

_____

_____

_____

_____

7. Does Ephesians 5:18 connect the concept of sobriety to both alcohol and mind-altering drugs like marijuana?

_____

_____

_____

_____

8. How can Christians use the teachings in the Bible to help others understand the importance of avoiding marijuana and other mind-altering substances?

_____

_____

_____

_____

_____

Group Discussion

1. What is the significance of our bodies being the temple of the Holy Spirit in relation to marijuana use?

   _____

   _____

   _____

   _____

   _____

2. What are the consequences of laziness according to the Bible? How does that apply to marijuana?

   _____

   _____

   _____

   _____

   _____

3. How does marijuana use make someone a slave to sin, and why is this problematic for Christians?

   _____

   _____

   _____

   _____

   _____

4. Why should Christians rely on God for peace and joy instead of using mind-altering substances like marijuana?

_____

_____

_____

_____

_____

5. What is the relationship between Christians and the government, and how does this apply to marijuana use?

_____

_____

_____

_____

_____

6. Considering the biblical reasons the book presents, should Christians say no to marijuana use?

_____

_____

_____

_____

_____

Reflection

_____

_____

_____

_____

_____

_____

_____

_____

_____

_____

_____

_____

_____

_____

_____

_____

_____

_____

CHAPTER 9

Why Be Sober?

Selected Scripture

"Do not get drunk on wine, which leads to debauchery. Instead, be filled with the Spirit." Ephesians 5:18 (NIV)

Application

This verse concerns alcohol, but scholars agree that the concept carries over to mind-altering drugs, including marijuana. This short passage gives us much information. The first part of the verse is a command not to be drunk. The second part tells us why. Because being drunk leads to debauchery—excessive indulgence in sin. The third part of the verse contrasts being drunk with being filled with the Spirit. It says you cannot have the Spirit and be drunk. The last part of the verse is also a command to be filled with the Spirit.

Many Bible passages call for Christians to be sober. First Thessalonians 5:6 says, "So then, let us not be like others, who are asleep, but let us be awake and sober." First Corinthians 15:34 says, "Become sober-minded as you ought, and stop sinning." In Romans 13:13, Paul calls us to behave decently and not be drunk.

Main Idea of Chapter

Not only does the Bible call us to be sober, but it also gives us many reasons to be sober. This chapter covers nine.

Chapter Summary

Christians are called to be sober because God is concerned with our well-being. The Bible outlines many reasons to maintain sobriety:

1. Drunkenness leads to poor judgment, leading to the consequences of poor decisions and sin.

2. Drunkenness leads to indulgence in sin, causing pain, misery, and death.

3. Being drunk or high is incompatible with being filled with the Holy Spirit.

4. Sobriety is necessary for effective prayer and maintaining a connection with God.

5. Drunkenness can result in poverty due to laziness, poor decision-making, and impaired job performance.

6. Drunkenness leads to losing spiritual insight.

7. A lack of sobriety can lead to a person not being saved, as the Bible states that drunks and drunkenness cannot enter the Kingdom of God.

8. Drunkenness makes one vulnerable to the enemy's attacks and susceptible to Satan's influence.

9. Mind-altering drugs, like marijuana, can open a person to the demonic realm, which is dangerous and contrary to biblical teachings.

God calls Christians to be sober because it helps them stay spiritually connected to Him, make better decisions, and avoid countless negative consequences in their lives. Sobriety is vital for maintaining a healthy spiritual life and relationship with God, as well as staying alert to the dangers of spiritual deception.

Terms

Debauchery: Excessive indulgence in sin.

Insight: The ability to gain accurate and deep intuitive understanding.

Judgment: The ability to make sensible decisions and conclusions.

Questions

1. How does a lack of sobriety lead to indulgence in sin?

_____

_____

_____

_____

_____

2. What is the connection between marijuana use and poor judgment?

_____

_____

_____

_____

_____

3. Knowing that Ephesians 5:18 contrasts drunkenness with being filled with the Spirit, can a person be under the influence of drugs or alcohol and be filled with the Holy Spirit?

_____

_____

_____

_____

_____

4. In what ways does drunkenness lead to the loss of spiritual insight?

_____

_____

_____

_____

_____

5. How does a lack of sobriety result in poor judgment? See Isaiah 28:7 and Proverbs 31:4-5.

_____

_____

_____

_____

_____

6. What is the relationship between substance abuse and poverty?

_____

_____

_____

_____

_____

7. In what ways does a lack of sobriety make a person more vulnerable to the enemy's attacks, as explained in 1 Peter 5:8?

_____

_____

_____

_____

_____

8. What is the historical significance of entheogens and *pharmakeia* in pagan religions and their connection to the spiritual world?

_____

_____

_____

_____

_____

9. Why is the Greek word *"pharmakeia"* translated as witchcraft?

_____

_____

_____

_____

_____

10. How does Galatians 5:19-21 warn against the use of *pharmakeia* (witchcraft)?

_____

_____

_____

_____

_____

11. How might Satan use drugs in the end times to deceive people, as mentioned in Revelation 18:23?

_____

_____

_____

_____

_____

12. What are some possible ways that marijuana use may contribute to the fulfillment of Revelation 18:23?

_____

_____

_____

_____

_____

13. How does marijuana use lead to the development of a warped sense of God and religion?

_____

_____

_____

_____

_____

14. What are the dangers of opening oneself up to the demonic realm through drug use, as warned by the Bible?

_____

_____

_____

_____

_____

15. How does Satan use the adverse effects of marijuana to destroy lives?

_____

_____

_____

_____

_____

16. In light of the various biblical reasons presented, why must Christians always remain sober?

_____

_____

_____

_____

_____

Group Discussion

1. Why does the Bible emphasize the importance of sobriety for Christians?

_____

_____

_____

_____

_____

2. How does substance abuse affect one's ability to pray effectively, as described in 1 Peter 4:7?

_____

_____

_____

_____

_____

3. Does drunkenness prevent people from entering the Kingdom of God, according to 1 Corinthians 6:10 and Galatians 5:21? Does this mean they cannot be saved?

_____

_____

_____

_____

_____

4. How do mind-altering drugs like marijuana open a person to the demonic realm, and why is this dangerous?

_____

_____

_____

_____

_____

5. Discuss your thoughts about Emma's story.

    _____

    _____

    _____

    _____

    _____

6. Paul calls us in Ephesians 4:15 to speak the truth in love. James 5:20 says, " . . . he who turns a sinner from the error of his way will save his soul from death and will cover a multitude of sins." With these scriptures in mind and knowing the spiritual pitfalls of marijuana, should Christians let others know about the dangers of marijuana?

    _____

    _____

    _____

    _____

    _____

7. How will you let others know about the dangers of marijuana? Who will you tell?

    _____

    _____

    _____

    _____

    _____

Reflection

_____

_____

_____

_____

_____

_____

_____

_____

_____

_____

_____

_____

_____

_____

_____

_____

_____

CHAPTER 10

Conclusion

Selected Scripture

"Be strong in the Lord and in the power of His might. Put on the whole armor of God, that you may be able to stand against the wiles (schemes) of the devil. For we do not wrestle against flesh and blood, but against principalities, against powers, against the rulers of the darkness of this age, against spiritual hosts of wickedness in the heavenly places. Therefore, take up the whole armor of God, that you may be able to withstand in the evil day." Ephesians 6:10-13

Application

Those who want the power to overcome any sin or addiction cannot neglect the spiritual component. One of the enemy's schemes is to lead people into addiction and keep them bound by that addiction. God is ready to help those who put on His armor overcome addiction.

What is the armor of God? Paul explains that in Ephesians 6:10-18. The picture Paul paints is not of a passive, Sunday-only, casual, lukewarm Christian. The image is of a person whose faith is in God alone, is full of the Spirit, is spiritually alert, and practices spiritual disciplines like prayer. Paul is saying that if you want to fail miserably at keeping destructive habits and sin out of your life, be a casual Christian or try to fight these battles on your own. Do not take care of the spiritual issue. Just put a Band-Aid on it. And you will fail, but if you want to stand strong against the enemy's attack, put on the whole armor of God; be a committed Christian, a true disciple of Jesus.

Main Idea of Chapter

When we weigh the potential benefits of marijuana versus the potential risks and harm, the evidence is overwhelmingly against marijuana. Marijuana is not something we should want in our bodies.

Chapter Summary

This book presents many arguments against marijuana use, highlighting its negative effects and associated risks. Adverse societal effects include organized crime, violence, accidents, and poverty. Marijuana may cause a temporary calm feeling in some people. Conversely, the numerous health issues include heart attacks, lung cancer, mental disorders, and addiction. Marijuana is a gateway drug and has no recognized medical use. It is still illegal under federal law despite laws in many states to the contrary.

The book also discusses biblical reasons to avoid marijuana use, emphasizing the importance of sobriety for Christians. Marijuana leads to laziness, enslavement to sin, and a reliance on something other than God—which is not God's plan. Sobriety is essential for spiritual growth and protection from sinful indulgence and the demonic realm.

This book gives tips on how to overcome marijuana addiction and recommends seeking the counsel of others, including pastors, teachers, and healthcare providers. Ignoring the spiritual aspect of one's life will lead to failure while surrendering to God and putting on His armor helps lead to victory over temptation and sin. We must make a conscious decision to trust in God and lean on Him rather than our own understanding.

No one is perfect, and everyone will occasionally fall short. However, God's love, mercy, grace, power, healing, and deliverance are available to those who repent and surrender their lives to Him.

When having difficulty quitting marijuana, one of the most important factors is not trying to quit on your own. Parents, pastors, counselors, teachers, and other mentors can help. DrWiggins.com/resources offers resources to help you quit.

Terms

Sin: Missing the mark. An immoral act that violates divine law. A transgression of God's law.

Temptation: A challenge to choose between right and wrong.

Questions

1. How does marijuana use impact an individual's mental health, such as anxiety or depression?

_____

_____

_____

_____

_____

2. Can you list some of the adverse medical effects of marijuana use, including heart and lung issues?

_____

_____

_____

_____

_____

3. How does marijuana use affect cognitive functions like memory, learning, attention, and decision-making?

_____

_____

_____

_____

_____

4. Can marijuana lead to schizophrenia?

_____

_____

_____

_____

_____

5. Why are vaping, edibles, and synthetic marijuana considered unsafe?

_____

_____

_____

_____

_____

6. What evidence supports the idea that marijuana has no recognized medical use and is addictive?

_____

_____

_____

_____

_____

7. Does marijuana act as a gateway drug? What evidence does
   the book give?

_____

_____

_____

_____

_____

8. Why does God call Christians to be sober, and how does marijuana use conflict with this calling?

_____

_____

_____

_____

_____

9. What role does the armor of God play in resisting temptation and maintaining spiritual well-being? Give biblical support.

_____

_____

_____

_____

_____

10. How do spiritual disciplines such as prayer, fasting, and worship help individuals overcome destructive habits and sin?

_____

_____

_____

_____

_____

11. What guidance does Proverbs offer regarding playing with the fire of sin?

_____

_____

_____

_____

_____

12. How can surrendering our life to God lead to overcoming temptation and sin?

_____

_____

_____

_____

13. What role does involvement in a Bible-believing church play in avoiding the pitfalls of marijuana use?

_____

_____

_____

_____

14. How have individuals you know relied on the power of God to overcome drug use, including marijuana?

_____

_____

_____

_____

_____

15. How can applying spiritual principles in this book help you and
    others avoid the negative consequences of marijuana use?

_____

_____

_____

_____

_____

Group Discussion

1. How many societal and economic reasons can you list not to
    smoke marijuana? (Chapter 1)

_____

_____

_____

_____

2. How many medical reasons can you list not to smoke marijuana?
    (Chapter 3)

_____

_____

_____

_____

_____

3. How many mental health reasons can you list not to smoke marijuana? (Chapter 4)

_____

_____

_____

_____

4. How many biblical reasons can you list not to smoke marijuana? (Chapters 7 through 9)

_____

_____

_____

_____

5. How can we overcome temptation and sin?

_____

_____

_____

_____

_____

6. Discuss your thoughts about Franklin's story.

_____

_____

_____

_____

_____

7. How has your view of marijuana changed since reading this book and participating in this study?

_____

_____

_____

_____

_____

8. What was your favorite part of this book and study?

_____

_____

_____

_____

_____

9. How will you apply what you have learned in this book to your life?

_____

_____

_____

_____

_____

10. How can you lead others to the truths found in this book?

_____

_____

_____

_____

_____

Reflection

_____

_____

_____

_____

_____

_____

Tips for Leaders

Congratulations on leading a group. This study is vitally important for today's culture. Countless lives are being devastated by marijuana. You will be amazed at the lives you can impact with the information in *Weeding Out the Myths About Marijuana, Expanded Edition: A Medical and Biblical Perspective*, and in this companion study guide.

Whether you have taught many Bible studies or this is your first, this study guide will be a great resource. Decide how many sessions you will have. I recommend at least six sessions. Otherwise, you will struggle to have time to cover and discuss the topics in sufficient detail. Decide the frequency of the meetings. Most groups meet weekly. Determine the location.

Before beginning the study, be sure each participant has a personal copy of the book *Weeding Out the Myths About Marijuana, Expanded Edition: A Medical and Biblical Perspective* and a copy of this companion study guide. Communicate with the group via group text, email, a group chat app, or something similar. Let the participants know how happy you are that they have chosen to join the group. Let them know the location of the meeting and the dates and times you will be meeting. Be sure everyone reads the group guidelines in this guide's Introduction.

Remind them to read the appropriate chapter or chapters in the book and the study guide. Emphasize the importance of doing the exercises and answering the questions before the study. Also, let them know not to get bogged down in difficult subjects or questions. The week before the meeting, send at least one reminder communication. Pray for the meetings and each member of the group. Encourage the group members to pray as well. God is moved by our prayers!

If this is a small group, many small groups have food as part of their meetings. You may be in charge of food for the meetings, or you may have another group member coordinate that. The food does not need to be anything elaborate or expensive. Chips and dip, chips and queso, finger sandwiches, veggie trays, fruit trays, cheese trays, cookies, and other desserts are fine for most groups.

The sessions are ready-made for you. I suggest the following basic schedule if you are teaching a small group. Begin with food and casual conversation. After ten to thirty minutes, gather the group together for the study. Greet the group. Thank them for coming. Make group and church-related announcements as appropriate. Take prayer requests (if appropriate). Pray over those requests and for the meeting.

Cover the material in the study guide. Read and briefly discuss the selected scripture and the application. Then, read the main idea of the chapter and the chapter summary. Immediately begin to ask the group study questions.

The chapter questions are for individual study. You will not have time to discuss those as a group. The chapter group study questions should be discussed as a group. There are many ways to do this. I like to read the question and ask for volunteers to answer. Some leaders go in a circle and have everyone answer each question. You will be very limited in the number of questions your group will cover using that method. Other leaders have each group member read a question and answer it. Some groups will only cover a few group questions and skip the other parts. There is no one right way. Ultimately, you can tailor this to your group. Time will be a significant factor. Many groups will be unable to cover each question, so choose the ones you feel are best for your group. Some groups may have only twenty to thirty minutes for discussion. Others will have an hour or more. Be mindful of your group members' time. Try not to go past the time you have set.

End the meeting with prayer and thank the group members for coming and participating. Invite them back for the next session and ask them to invite a friend.

About the Author

Raymond Wiggins, MD, DDS, MDiv is a licensed physician. He has been on the front lines of patient care for almost three decades and has performed general anesthetics on more than 27,000 patients, including thousands of marijuana users. He has two doctorates—an MD from McGovern Medical School and a DDS from Texas A&M School of Dentistry. He recently earned his MDiv (Master of Divinity) in New Testament Studies from Regent University.

Seeing the devastating and deadly effects of marijuana on his patients, family, and friends, Dr. Wiggins began investigating the subject, and what he found shocked him. His search for answers revealed overwhelming evidence showing the adverse effects of marijuana.

Soon, he found he was not alone. As people learned of his quest, many had similar stories of friends and family who had suffered harm or died from this drug. Every heartbreaking story is fuel on a fire that cannot be quenched. Dr. Wiggins has the expertise to evaluate the mountains of information about marijuana, weed out the myths, and present the truth about the subject in an understandable, informative, persuasive, and engaging manner. His mission is to save as many people as possible from the physical, mental, and spiritual ravages of this drug. He believes if he saves one life, it is worth the effort.

Dr. Wiggins serves on his state board Dental Review Committee and on the Edward C. Hinds Academy Foundation board. He has served on the Texas Society of Oral and Maxillofacial Surgeons board.

Dr. Wiggins is available for speaking engagements and interviews. To learn more about him and his latest projects, visit DrWiggins.com. Sign up for his connection email list and follow him on social media.

Books by Raymond Wiggins MD, DDS, MDiv

Dr. Wiggins has written two editions of his book, *Weeding Out the Myths About Marijuana*, with a companion study guide for each. The information below will help you determine which ones are best for you or your group.

Weeding Out the Myths About Marijuana
This book tells the truth about marijuana and other cannabis products from a medical and scientific perspective in an easy-to-read, enjoyable manner. This standard edition was written for use in public schools, law enforcement agencies, other government agencies, and for those only wanting the medical perspective and who do not want to learn about the spiritual implications of cannabis. This edition limits or eliminates biblical and spiritual content to allow for use in secular institutions.

The Official Study Guide for Weeding Out the Myths About Marijuana
This study guide is for use with the companion standard edition and is great for strictly secular group or personal study. Public schools, secular community youth programs, and secular addiction treatment and recovery programs will find this study guide an essential resource. Those wanting a deeper understanding about the subject of marijuana will want this resource.

Weeding Out the Myths About Marijuana, Expanded Edition: A Medical and Biblical Perspective
This book tells the truth about marijuana and other cannabis products from a medical, scientific, **and biblical** perspective in an easy-to-read,

enjoyable manner. The Expanded Edition contains the medical information from the standard edition. This edition contains three additional chapters covering a biblical perspective about marijuana. This edition also contains more heartwarming true stories and expanded versions of the ones in the standard edition. This is the edition most people will prefer.

The Official Study Guide for Weeding Out the Myths About Marijuana, Expanded Edition: A Medical and Biblical Perspective

This study guide is for use with the companion Expanded Edition and is great for most personal or group study. Most, small and large church groups, community youth programs, colleges, universities, private schools, addiction treatment and recovery programs, and others will find this study guide an essential resource. Those wanting a deeper understanding about the subject of marijuana and its scientific, medical, and spiritual implications will want this resource.